The Story of a Natural History EXPEDITION

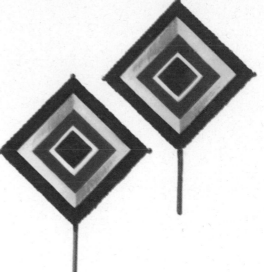

The
Story of a
Natural History

EXPEDITION

Written and illustrated by
RUSSELL FRANCIS PETERSON

Doubleday & Company, Inc., Garden City, New York

ACKNOWLEDGMENT

The Author wishes to express his gratitude and appreciation for the opportunities afforded in the field background of this book to The American Museum of Natural History, especially to Dr. Harold E. Anthony, Mr. Leonard J. Brass, Mr. Hobart M. Van Deusen, Dr. Richard G. Van Gelder, and Mr. John C. Pallister for their guidance, advice and encouragement; and to Philip Spalding for his generosity and valued assistance.

Contents

Preface

The word "expedition" is derived from the Latin word "expeditus," which means "to free one caught by the foot." We are all of us "caught by the foot" in some manner and cannot often go where we might like, for we are bound to school, a job, raising a family, or some other duty which binds us to home. To "go on an expedition" to some exotic foreign land has, at one time or another, been a dream common to us all. But few of us ever go; we simply dream and remain "caught by the foot."

This is a book about an expedition. It is the story of a natural history expedition. Its purposes are to show you how and why expeditions function and, in a way, to tell you how *you*, if you dream hard enough and work hard enough, can be a part of such a journey. There is no "short cut," just as there is no easy way to medicine or to the study of law, but there is a way.

And it is not yet too late. Even as rockets probe the depths of outer space, there are still cannibals and head-hunters and tribes that wield stone axes and fight with arrows and spears. There is still danger and there is still opportunity. There are yet landfalls on tropical islands unchanged since the eighteenth century, when Cook, an English naval captain, explored many of the beautiful and remote atolls of the South Seas. There are mountains as yet unconquered, and galaxies still unknown, and even when these are gone, there will remain other unconquered things.

AUTHOR'S NOTE. *Certain scientific names are included in this book in places where the animals are so rare or little known that a common name alone might leave some doubt as to their exact identity.*

Over Tropic Seas

The great expanse of Pacific Ocean which separates America from Australia is no longer, by its size, a threat to mariners. Modern passenger ships have reduced passage time to two weeks instead of months, and airplanes have shrunk time into hours. But that great ocean is just as wide and just as deep as it was in Magellan's day. If your mode of transportation is not jet plane or sleek passenger ship, you will get to know that ocean well. A cargo vessel takes over a month to reach Australia, stopping at many ports along the way. And it is aboard such a ship that our expedition leaves New York harbor, bound for faraway New Guinea.

Cargo is taken aboard and unloaded at many ports, and there is much of interest going on aboard such a ship. Each port is different and is a wonderful experience. The northeastern harbors are cold and smell of oil. The ports of the southern United States are warm and smell of fruit and lumber. As you pass through the Panama Canal and visit the first tropical towns, the air is laden with the scent of spices and with the sounds of exotic birds.

Much later, after long days on a sparkling sea under trade-wind clouds, you cross the equator and reach faraway Tahiti, with its pungent scents of copra, or dried coconut, and the delicate aroma of flowers that is borne to the ship by a gentle land breeze.

Another week will bring you to New Zealand, with its strange kiwi birds and magnificent mountains. And finally you reach Australia, "Land of the Upside Down"—for there you must go *north* into the tropics. The ship will stop at Sydney and Brisbane and then continue along the Australian Great Barrier Reef, where teeming bird life, great sharks, and brilliantly colored fishes are to be seen. Perhaps you will be fortunate enough to see the spout and dark back of a gigantic whale.

At last the ship approaches the dense tropical coast of New Guinea, the world's second largest island. Mist-wreathed mountains, dark and forbidding, reach down to the sea. Waves crash upon the coral sand and brilliant parrots fly swiftly through the jungle trees. The ship glides through a passage in the jagged coral reefs and secures its great hawsers to the pier at Port Moresby. We have arrived at our base of operations.

Into the Jungle

New Guinea is one of the world's largest islands. It is an undeveloped country in the heart of the equatorial tropics and is governed by two countries. The western half is governed by the Netherlands, and the eastern half is divided into two sections; the southern sector, Papua, is an Australian Territory, while the northern, known as New Guinea, is under the administration of Australia by the authority of the United Nations. Our expedition has applied for permission to enter the Australian half of New Guinea. Port Moresby is the capital city of the Australian Territory and all government offices are to be found there. It is a modern seaport town with modern buildings, but the jungle reaches to its edge and the streets are filled with colorful native people, as well as with people from other parts of the world.

In New Guinea the native people are very primitive. They wear few clothes, because it is very warm, and their houses are made of palm leaves or grass. The Australian government is doing much to give the native people schools and hospitals of their own, but their customs and life remain quite different from ours. In Port Moresby these different lives mix.

PACIFIC OCEAN

HOLLANDIA

NORTHEAST NEW GUINEA

GUINEA

AUSTRALIAN PAPUA

LAE

PORT MORESBY

CORAL SEA

AUSTRALIA

TOWNSVILLE

Natives in feather-and-shell headdresses are seen crossing streets between passing motorcars. There are native policemen in smart military dress. Jungle drums can be heard on a corner where a drugstore or a gas station stands. Life is changing in this green land—but only a few miles away are villages which seldom see civilization, and in the interior are people who have never seen a white man. New Guinea is very mountainous and there are few roads into the hills. Airplanes fly over these great mountains, but it is difficult or impossible to approach the peaks by land.

At Port Moresby our expedition must see many people in government positions and arrange with merchants for supplies that we could not bring from America. Our cargo is unloaded and brought to a warehouse for field-packing, and we must see to the hiring of native personnel.

11

Besides a staff of trained scientists, an expedition must have a staff of native helpers. Because scientists work all day and much of the night on their complicated projects, people must be employed to cook and to act as assistants. Natives in New Guinea are intelligent and quick to learn, and even if they cannot speak your language, they make valuable helpers. Each scientist usually has two or more native helpers: the mammal collector has a "shoot boy" and a "skinning boy." The botanist has a "flower-flower boy" and the herpetologist has a "gai-gai boy" ("gai-gai" means "snake" in a native tongue and is pronounced *"guy-guy"*). Each boy knows his job well, once he is taught, and is very proud of his position.

Often a local white man is employed to act as a guide and as an interpreter, for the native languages differ greatly. The principal language spoken at Port Moresby is *Motu* and the main language on the northern coast is *Pidgin.* But there are also many different languages unrelated to these.

When all the necessary things involving government and people are done, the field-packing must be begun. We completely unpack our cargo from its great shipping cases and spread it out on a wide expanse of floor. Then we reassemble it all in our special museum boxes and in duffel bags with carrying straps. The entire cargo must be broken down into "carrying loads," boxes or bags which can be carried by one man or by two men carrying a box between them. This is necessary because, once away from roads and transportation, everything must be carried through the jungle by men employed as "carriers." The Australian Territorial government is very strict about native carriers and has a rule that one man is not allowed to carry over thirty-five pounds and two men with a pole not over seventy pounds. Thirty-five pounds is not much for a man to *lift,* but it is a great deal of weight to carry over steep mountains. There is also a firm law regulating food and clothing for native personnel.

While some of the scientific party are packing for the field, others will go on an air survey of the particular mountain valley in which the work will be done. Since there are no roads anywhere near the area, the hired expedition airplane must land in the next valley and the scientific party must climb a mountain range before arriving at the work area. This range is flown over, and the stream to be followed is mapped from the air. Streams or water courses of any kind are always used as "paths" because all animals as well as people need water nearby. Dangerous places on the proposed path and any native villages are noted on the map. Then the plane returns to Port Moresby and last details are set in order.

At last everything and everyone are ready. All of the men and equipment are moved out to the airstrip and are put aboard a DC-3. The plane leaves the landing strip with a roar and quickly enters the low clouds. Soon it has flown much higher and emerges into brilliant sunshine. Below lies a sea of billowing white clouds with majestic green peaks rising up through it. The native boys are not nervous, even though this is their first airplane flight. They talk in their own language and eagerly point at the tiny villages far below.

In two hours the airplane descends through bumpy air and finally rolls to a stop on a green field two miles from a small village. Everyone alights and helps to unload the hundreds of pounds of equipment. Carrier boys are eager to be chosen and all of the villagers and many of their friends from other villages line up and puff out their chests to show how strong they are. Forty of the strongest men are chosen and quickly follow instructions through the interpreter to carry all the equipment to the village. We can see a native path, which is called a "track," leading into the jungle. The great forest and dark mountains look forbidding. We all wave good-by to the pilot of the plane and watch the aircraft quickly disappear in the distance. Then we turn and follow the carriers up to the village.

Rain Forest

This mountain village to which we have come is several hundred feet above the valley floor, between high mountain ranges. Great peaks reach skyward and are lost in the clouds. The village is comprised of only nine houses made of poles and grass. The houses are simple, but they are beautifully woven and thatched with fine grass and coconut leaves. Pigs are everywhere. Children dart about and chase the noisy dogs. An old man sits in a doorway and softly taps a drum.

The carriers whom we have followed to the village have laid down the heavy equipment and are resting. When we arrive, we go to the house of the village chief, or "luluai," and "pay our respects" to him just as we would to a government official. In fact, although he is wearing feathers and displaying a bone through his nose, he *is* the local government representative, for he wears a large brass medal, hung about his neck, which reads "V.C." This stands for "Village Counselor" and the Territorial Government wisely gives him this honor so as to make someone responsible for happenings in that area. This country is far too remote for government police, although several times during the year an official New Guinea Patrol Officer does visit the village to act as magistrate and uphold the law. There is also appointed from among the village men a Native Policeman, who lives in the village. The man wears a dark blue uniform, consisting of a "lava-lava," or skirt, a shirt of the same material, and a military belt and cap. He is responsible for keeping order while the Patrol Officer is not there. But it is the Village Counselor who is the official to whom we offer our greeting and from whom we receive our welcome to the village.

Since it is still early in the day, we plan to leave for the mountains almost immediately. Our transport man calls out orders in the native language and the carriers are assembled in military fashion. Each man shoulders his burden and we start upward on a narrow path through the steep gardens the natives cultivate near the village. Even though our plane landed at a height of six thousand feet, our map shows we must yet climb over four thousand feet in order to cross the mountain range which separates us from the next valley.

The path is very steep and slippery. The stones are loose and the foliage is very thick and wet. We climb upward very slowly. By late afternoon we reach the top of the dividing range. It is rocky and sharp, almost like the edge of a giant knife. The trees are small, bent and twisted, and covered with wet moss. There is a heavy mist, and it is quite cold. The carriers shiver in spite of the wool shirts we have provided, and we carefully descend over the steep edge of the divide.

But it is too late in the day to go farther. We hurriedly pitch a makeshift camp in the hollow of two ridges, have a makeshift meal, roll up in our sleeping bags, and quickly go to sleep.

Early next morning we hurry on. We must make a permanent camp as quickly as possible so that our work may begin.

As we descend into our valley, the trees again grow high and we enter a very thick region known as Rain Forest. This name is given to a certain type of dense foliage cover that is found only in tropics where it is very warm and where there is much rainfall. It is different from anything in temperate regions and is true "jungle." Giant trees with spreading "boles," or bases, rise to great heights, shutting out the sun except for scattered rays which pierce the gloom. Vines and creepers, ferns, flowers, and many kinds of unusual plants all make a Rain Forest a strange and wonderful place. Brightly hued tropical birds flash through the trees like swift bursts of color and fill the air with their strident calls.

Iridescent butterflies and sprays of orchids are everywhere. It is truly a wonderland—but it is very wet.

There is moisture everywhere. The rainfall is very heavy and very frequent. But in between these showers the sun shines brightly on the forest. This combination of water and sun makes everything grow and grow. It is midsummer every day of the year in the tropics, and growth is a never ending process.

Although the canopy of treetops is very thick, the ground far below, where we walk, is quite bare, except for shrubs and a leafy cover. Since most of the light is shut out from above, the lesser ground plants do not have a chance to grow.

We decide to make our first camp at the edge of the Rain Forest on the site of an ancient village, still planted with coconuts and partially cleared. Behind our camp, the Rain Forest looms dark and forbidding, while below us the sun shines brightly on the "savannah," or grasslands.

There is much to be done, for large-scale scientific work cannot be carried out from inadequate camps. Tents are erected for shelter, a "cookhouse" is made of native materials, and a dining area is cleared, for sleep and food are essential to good work. All our damp clothes are washed and then dried in the sun. There are also many smaller tasks, such as filling water bags, setting up kerosene pressure lamps, and digging refuse pits. Long work tables are made from split pandanus poles and tied together with strips of pliable bark.

Much of our food is brought with us. Tinned meat, flour, salt, rice, and other staples are not to be had unless they are carried into the jungle. But a great part of our meals consists of native food—yams, lemons, bananas, coconuts, taro root, and queer leaves from a tree that when cooked taste like spinach.

Soon the aroma of fresh bread fills the camp. In a short while our corner of the jungle that we call "home" is sheltered, lighted and protected.

The Daylight Hours

In the cool morning air the view from our campsite is breath-taking. The open grasslands of the valley are covered with a thick, low-hanging mist which gives the appearance of a clouded lake. The Rain Forest at the valley's edge is filtered with light and shadow and rises steeply on the mountain side to meet the billowing clouds which surround the top ranges. Above these clouds the jagged peaks cut sharply upward and glisten in the sudden brilliance of the morning's first light. There is beauty everywhere, but if the scientist stopped often to contemplate natural wonders, very little work would be done.

With all camping essentials now finished, each man prepares his private "laboratory." These areas must be set apart from each other because of the different work being done in them. If a sudden wind arises while delicate insect specimens are being handled, fragile wings may be broken and all may be made worthless. If the sun is too hot while the mammalogist works at skinning small animals, the skin may dry out too soon; or if there is too much shade, specimens may mildew. Many considerations are necessary before making the separate work areas ready.

With each morning of the months spent in the field, there is the same pattern of things to be done. There are three principal functions: to collect specimens; to "prepare" or preserve them scientifically so that they will not spoil; and to make many notes and study not only the specimens but their "ecology," or natural surroundings.

Sulphur-crested White Cockatoo

Now that our base camp is functioning smoothly, we begin work. We first follow the search for birds and snakes. It may seem odd to mix birds and snakes. They have very little in common, it is true. But they are both on the "daytime list." Although there are nocturnal, or nighttime, birds as well as reptiles, most of these animals are lovers of the sun, and our trail begins at daybreak.

The Rain Forest is very rich in bird life. The forest aisles echo from dawn to dark with birdcalls of every kind. As we push our way through the wet leaves, dashing fine drops of water in every direction, we are startled by vivid red and green fruit pigeons as they explode from the undergrowth and flash noisily past us. Sulphur-crested cockatoos scream a warning at our approach and "rainbird" cuckoos (so called because the natives think they bring rain) fly swiftly overhead. We hear a crashing of

21

New Guinea Hornbill

Rosenberg's Honey-sucker

leaves and branches and see five great hornbills fly from a giant fig tree. Their wings make a curious sound as of strumming rubber bands and swish violently as they fly. The male hornbill's head and neck are reddish yellow, while the female's are all black. The hornbill is about the size of the American bald eagle though less heavy in proportion.

Brilliant parrots fly overhead or perch on mossy branches. One of them, the Lorius Parrot, is particularly interesting for it reverses the usual pattern in birds in which the male is nearly always more colorful than the female. Then there is the vibrantly blue Racket-tail Kingfisher and many strange types of larger birds.

Lorius Parrot

Robust Whistler

Galatea Racket-tail

Blackcapped Lory

There is a continual sprinkling of small birds surrounding you like raindrops in the sun. Very tiny sunbirds with glistening black and scarlet throats fly from vine to vine eating flower nectar. Flycatchers dart from their perches and turn into pinwheels of color trying to catch the insects that they feed upon. On the ground an oddly shaped, plump little bird called a "Pitta" sings loudly but manages to hide when you come near.

Bird collecting is done with great care. Many birds are rare and must be carefully protected if future generations are to know them at all. Much of the collecting is done by native assistants trained to treat the specimens with great respect.

Black Sun-bird

White-eye

Blue-breasted Pitta

23

A great deal of the valuable work on rare birds is done with the aid of cameras. Many kinds of cameras are used to take both movies and still pictures. "Blinds" are constructed to keep the photographer out of sight of the bird subjects while pictures are taken of nesting activities, feeding, and "courtship dances."

As we go on, we must also keep alert for signs of reptiles. Snakes are *not,* as most people think, easily found in the jungle. Of all the animal life collected on such trips, snakes seem always to be more rare in numbers than any other kind of life. This is partly because they are so elusive. They have sensitive sound organs and, under ordinary conditions, hear you coming through the underbrush long before you are close enough to see them. Few snakes are of aggressive temperament, although nearly all are relatively fearless when trod upon or when they are surprised at close range. A great many New Guinea snakes are poisonous, however, and two of these, the taipan and the death adder, are among the most dangerous snakes in the world. Care must always be taken when walking in places which might hide a dangerous snake.

The first snake we come upon—and only after hours of searching—is a whip snake. The body of this dark, striped snake is only slightly thicker than a pencil, but he is over four feet long. He has large eyes and can move quickly. He is poisonous, so he must be handled with extreme caution. The snake's head is first held down tightly with a stick, while his wildly lashing tail is caught. Then he is grasped firmly behind the head and quickly put into a heavy bag and securely tied. Even to a trained herpetologist there is a measure of relief when the job is finally done.

Death Adder

Natives have a strong fear of snakes, and the word "gai-gai" is enough to freeze them motionless or have them jump wildly aside. Of course, snakes are a far greater hazard to natives, who wear so few clothes and go barefoot. Our party is well clothed in long khaki pants and shirts with long sleeves, as well as in high, nailed leather boots.

Two other snakes are captured nearby, and another later in the day. One is a small, dark brown snake with an orange head, only a foot long; and the other is a New Guinea green python which is one of the most vividly colored of all snakes. It is large—six to eight feet long—and it is a bright emerald green. It has a few white markings on the dorsal ridge, or center of its back. It often goes unseen among the green leaves, but once caught away from cover, it is very conspicuous. The fourth snake, caught later, is the great amethystine python—over fourteen feet long with coils like a steel trap. Fortunately, he is not poisonous, but capturing him is no easy matter.

All of these things are fascinating to see—but the most magnificent inhabitants of the Rain Forest are the birds of paradise. They are among the true wonders of the bird world, and can be described but poorly in words. There are over thirty-nine species, but few are to be seen at any one place. They are found on the island of New Guinea, in a small portion of Australia, and in no other place in the world. If you move quietly as you penetrate the thick forest, you may see the splendid Greater Bird of Paradise displaying his flaring red plumes. These plumes are part of the bird's "side feathers," under its wings, and can be spread into a great fan or gathered into a trailing spray. Only the male bird is blessed with this array—the female bird is very plain and drab in comparison. She is brown with no plumes and no spectacular colors. You may also see the yellow-plumed Bird of Paradise. The Blue Bird of Paradise has a white eye ring and blue plumes, and the black Ribbon-tail Bird of Paradise has a long, streaming white tail. The King Bird of Paradise is smaller, but is a brilliant scarlet and white and has blue feet. It is difficult to believe that a near relative of these gems of form and color is the common crow!

**Ribbon-tail
Bird of Paradise**

**Little King
Bird of Paradise**

Early in the afternoon we return to camp, our footsteps muffled in the damp leaves. Because we are silent as we walk, we surprise many other animals on the path. Occasionally a lizard streaks away before us and there is a wild chase to capture him. Frogs are also caught as they blunder from the damp shadows.

Finally we come out of the forest into the sunshine and back to our dry camp. Our specimens are safely put aside to await preparation.

Greater Bird of Paradise

Hours of Darkness

Night comes quickly in the jungle. It is almost as though a light were switched off. Suddenly, where even in the daylight there were shadows and gloom, it becomes black night. Our pressure lamps brightly illuminate the pale green tents and make a cheery oasis of friendly light. When we go outside of that warmly lit circle, our powerful battery lamps pierce the darkness and make brilliant paths for us to follow. These lamps are much the same as a miner's lamp, being attached to our heads by a strong band while the five batteries are carried on our belts. Wherever we turn our heads, there is light. With these remarkable lamps we are free to walk in the jungle or over dangerous rocks as safely at night as though it were broad daylight, and there is the added convenience of having both hands free. In this way our work goes on around the clock.

However black and forbidding the New Guinea jungle appears, those who hunt after dark know there is little danger from animals. There are, of course, very dangerous snakes, but there are no large land mammals in New Guinea. No tigers or leopards or rhinoceroses live here. There are not even monkeys. For this great island is part of the Australian region, and its animals, as well as its trees and nearly everything else, are different from any in the world. Over one third of all its mammals are "marsupials," or pouched animals, such as the kangaroo. The kangaroo is "large"—but not when compared with a tiger. And in New Guinea not even large kangaroos are found; there are only a small relative of the kangaroo called a wallaby and the strange tree-climbing kangaroo. It seems amusing to know that the most dangerous animal found in the New Guinea jungles is an ordinary pig! However, it is less amusing to find that this pig has great curving tusks which can easily kill a man.

Nearly all New Guinea mammals are strange to us. The spiny ant-eater, or *echidna* (e-*kid*-na), an ancient egg-laying mammal similar to the platypus, probes for worms with a long "bill." There is a strange possum called a *cuscus* (cuss-cuss), which hangs by its tail. There are giant rats larger than a cat, and giant bats with great wings reaching to nearly six feet. And there are "ordinary" rats and squirrel-like animals which we would think worthless—but which are to museums more valuable than a cage full of tigers.

Some of these mammals are collected with guns at night. Others are trapped at night, but the traps must be set before darkness falls. For any larger animals, live cage traps are sometimes used. But for the small rats, an ordinary rattrap is better than any other method. These traps kill the animal, but kill it instantly and without suffering. They are set in "lines," or series, as are those that fur trappers use. They are baited with a mixture of peanut butter, oatmeal, and bacon in late afternoon, while there is still light to see where the animal tracks and tunnels might be. But it is not until morning that we will know what has been caught.

Sand Wallaby

At dawn, the mammalogist is out to inspect his traps. The long line begins in the grasslands, goes upward through the Rain Forest, and returns by the banks of a rushing Rain Forest stream. The trap line is marked by freshly cut leaves or by wisps of cotton impaled on branches.

The first set of traps is in a grassy patch below the camp. The first trap is sprung, but empty. The second and third are untouched, except that the bait has been eaten by ants. The fourth is sprung, and held in it, killed instantly by the powerful spring, is a brown rat with coarse hair, named *Rattus*.

Dactylopsila: Striped Marsupial Possum

Distoechurus:
Feather-tailed Possum

The animal trappers leave the grass and follow their last night trail into the Rain Forest. The first trap holds another rat, *Pogonomys* (po-*gon*-o-mis), but this is a tree rat and an entirely different animal. More suggestive of a squirrel than a rat, it has a "prehensile" or grasping tail. Further on we capture a very rare animal named *Distoechurus* (dis-toe-*kur*-us), the Pygmy Feather-tailed Possum. Very tiny, still it is a marsupial and has a small pouch. Its tail is "feathered" like an arrow shaft, with long hairs forming an edge only on the sides. We also climb a tree to find *Petaurus* (pet-*or*-us), the little Sugar Glider, which looks like our flying squirrel but is a marsupial.

Pogonomys: Prehensile Tree Rat

Phalanger: Spotted Cuscus

Satanellus: Native Cat

Petaurus: Sugar Glider

Dendrolagus: Tree-climbing Kangaroo

We are most fortunate in capturing a tree-climbing kangaroo, *Dendrolagus* (den-dro-*la*-gus). These richly colored animals are unique, in that they are a highly specialized branch of their family. They are ungainly on the ground, but fast and agile in the trees.

In a trap set close to a rushing mountain stream we find *Hydromys* (*hi*-dro-mis), the Water Rat. He is very dark and robust, and looks much like a small otter. His tail is strangely marked, being black for half its length, then pure white to its tip. We also find traces of other kinds of rats; from the giant tree-climbing varieties to the dark, chestnut-colored burrowing rats. All of these rare animals called "rats" are far from the loathsome quadruped we know as a rat; some of these delicate creatures are among the most cleanly and handsome of small mammals.

Peroryctes: Striped Bandicoot

In the murky shadows of a decaying log, the trappers find yet another new animal. This one is exciting, for it is a "marsupial rat." It is really not a rat at all but is called that because it most resembles one. A "rat" is only a "rat" because his teeth make him one. "Dentition," or the arrangement of teeth, is the principal basis by which animals are scientifically classified. Of course, there are other considerations in judging what an animal is, such as the length and breadth of the skull, the color of the fur, and all measurements in comparison with other kinds of animals; but it is mainly the skull that is the basis of comparison. The name "rat" is derived from the genus *Rattus,* and it is well known to us only because it is a very common type of mammal. But if an animal looks like a rat, and acts like a rat, and seems like a rat in every way except that it has not got teeth like a rat, then it is not a rat. This "marsupial rat" not only has a pouch but its teeth are very different from those of anything else. Its name is *Murexia* (muir-*ex*-ia); its fur is brown and its nose is curiously pointed. It is a valued prize for the collection.

The Rain Forest trail also yields things which are in no way like rats. A trap baited with meat has caught an animal of fantastic color and shape. Its fur is a rich brown spotted with many small polka dots of white. On the dark leaves where he has been caught he is very conspicuous. But when we move him into the patches of sunlight which filter through the foliage, we see that his "protective coloration" makes him nearly invisible. His scientific name is *Satanellus* (satan-*ell*-us), which means "devil-like," for he has a most vicious temper. Although he, too, is a marsupial, his nature is far different from the placid possum or bounding wallaby. He resembles a ferret, or weasel-like animal, and is built for both power and speed.

Skulls are made of many separate bones which are joined together as is a jigsaw puzzle. The drawing at the left is a rat's skull. All skulls are joined in the same way.

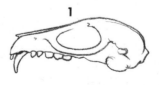

Above 1) a dog's skull and 2) a rat's skull showing differences in tooth structure.

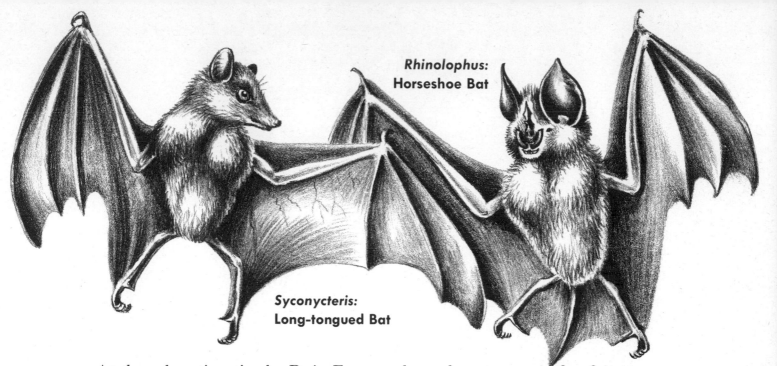

Rhinolophus: Horseshoe Bat

Syconycteris: Long-tongued Bat

At three locations in the Rain Forest, where the canopy roof or forest cover descends lower than at other places, we have stretched nets of fine silk across the path. These ensnare small bats, which at night follow the path in their flight and fly low to avoid the overhanging leaves. We capture two: one is a small, light tan bat with large eyes and a face like a dog, and the other is one which could be called "ugly," for he has very small eyes, large ears, and a curious "leaf" of flesh on his nose. The dog-faced bat is *Syconycteris* (sigh-con-*ic*-teris), a flower and fruit eater. Far from being "blind," as superstitions lead people to believe all bats are, this flying animal has good eyes and flies through the jungle mainly by sight. He has sharp doglike teeth with which to tear open the hard skin casings of wild fruits, and a long, pliable tongue to take the nectar from flowers.

The other bat feeds on flying insects. His name is *Rhinolophus*. (rhino-*lo*-phus). His eyes are small and weak, for he does not use them as does our fruit bat. Instead, he has well-developed ears that act as a radar device, receiving the echo of his continued small squeaks, which bounce back from trees and other objects in time for him to turn and avoid them. And, in the same manner, these returning sounds tell him where insects are in the dark night air and lead him to them so that he can quickly capture them with his sharp teeth. His very strange "nose leaf" is thought to act as a sort of radar antenna to guide the sounds to his ears.

As we return to camp we see our other native assistant approaching. He has spent the night at a high elevation and is just now returning with his catch. His approach causes much excitement, for he has captured a mountain wallaby named *Dorcopsulus* (dor-*cop*-sulus), a striped possum named *Dactylopsila* (dac-tee-*lop*-silla), and a small, long-nosed bandicoot. These additional animals make it necessary to begin scientific preparation as soon as our hurried breakfast is finished.

Tree Frog

Preserving Specimens

The preparation table is the "command center" of an expedition. The collection of specimens is strictly limited to the number that can be properly preserved for study. Even one extra specimen would be a wasted life. A zoological park keeps specimens alive; a museum keeps specimens which cannot be kept alive. They both exist for only one purpose: to teach us things which we should know. They are libraries of *things* instead of books. It would be far better to have everything kept alive. How wonderful it would be to be able to see a live prehistoric dinosaur! Since this cannot be, we can only preserve what we can. The thousands of different things which are stored by a museum and similar institutions number so many that they cannot all be kept alive or in their natural state. When a koala bear, a rare and exquisite animal from Australia, is brought to America, it is not only kept alive in a specially prepared place but many doctors and experts are called in to see that it remains in good health and that it lives well. There is only one koala bear in all the world. But when a different rat is brought from far away, such preparations are not possible. Why? Because there are many, many rats. It is not the rat's fault. There are just not enough facilities to go around. But in these days of research on cancer and other human diseases, no rat or small animal is insignificant no matter how "ugly" or how remote it may be from our own lives.

New Guinea Green Python

Satanellus: Native Cat

And so, lying on our preparation tables are dead animals. As the sun warms them, it speeds the forces of decomposition. We have collected birds, mammals, snakes, lizards, and frogs. If they are left more than a few hours, they will rot and be worthless. Decomposition is a force of nature. As soon as the magic spark of life goes out, decomposition crumbles the body and soon turns muscle and skin into a simple substance which blends with the earth. This spoilage never can be fully stopped and decomposition will eventually win out and return things to the earth and their natural state. But decomposition can be postponed. Certain things, such as small frogs, seem to shrivel before our eyes. To preserve these animals before they spoil is a race against time.

There are three ways to preserve animals: to freeze the animal, to use a liquid preservative, or to dry out, or "mummify." Freezing is not practical because it cannot readily be done and because decomposition sets in as soon as the animal is brought into warmth. Liquid preservative causes stiffness and eventually takes away all color. Mummifying leaves hair and color, but hopelessly dries out skin and internal tissues. Both of these two latter methods must be used if study of the specimen is to be complete.

First, many measurements must be made, for all preservation tends to either shrink or expand the specimen to some degree. The total length and the tail and hind foot measurements are first taken. If it is a bird, the wings are measured; and, if a snake, the distances from the anal plate to the head and then to the tip of the tail are taken. Then the specimen is weighed—always by the metric system, which is universally used by scientists. A permanent field number is given to each specimen, recording whether it is male or female; the day, month, and year captured; the exact location of its capture; and by whom it was caught. If any of this information is lost, the preserved animal loses much of its value. Only after all these things are done does any kind of preservation begin.

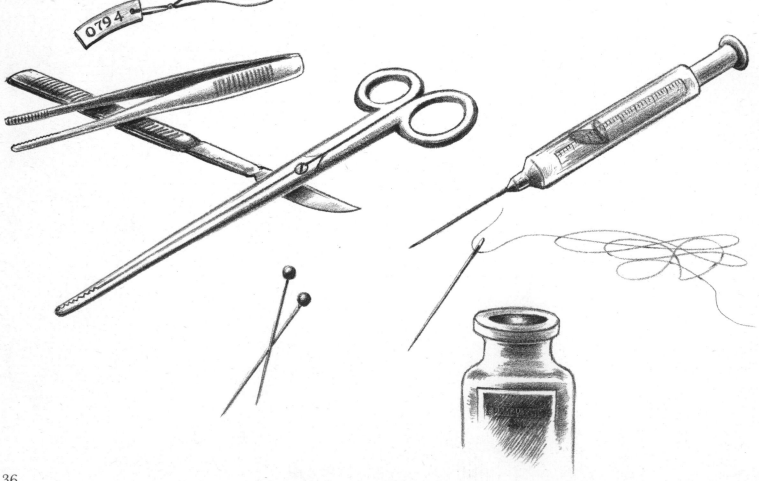

Liquid preservation can employ any of a number of things, but those chiefly used are alcohol and formaldehyde. These liquid gases (for that is what they are) are first mixed with water and then injected into the animal's inner parts, into all muscles, and even under the skin. For this a hypodermic syringe and hollow needle are used. Finally, the entire animal must be put into a mixture of the type of liquid being used, and permanently kept there.

Mummifying, or drying, an animal is more complicated. Seldom is the whole animal dried. Nearly always just the skin and feet are preserved; the inner parts are not used. The skull, being the "key" and most important part of the animal, is always kept and carefully cleaned. All the meat and muscle tissue is removed, the brain cavity is cleaned, and the skull is separately dried. The skin of the animal is removed by making an incision with a scalpel on the underside. Care is taken not to cut into the body wall where the powerful gastric juices and intestines are located, for the skin fits the body like a glove and it is not necessary to cut into that area, where ferment and decomposition are taking place more rapidly than on the outside. The leg bones are cut through and kept with the skin. The skin is turned inside out and pulled over the head. It is cut off finally at the nose. The skin, with cleaned tail and legs attached, is very light and feels about like a lady's neckpiece of soft fur.

Once off, the skin is poisoned with a strong alkaline powder, such as borax, to keep insects from eating it. The skin is then turned fur side out and is stuffed with a hemplike substance called "tow." Sometimes cotton is used for this process. Enough tow, or cotton, is used to fill out the body to normal proportions. An artificial tail bone of wire is inserted in the tail, and the cut which was made in the body is sewn up with needle and thread. The animal is then pinned to a board and dried in the sun.

Both birds and mammals are preserved in this manner. All of the beautiful birds and lifelike animals you see mounted in museum halls came from field skins such as these. But reptiles are nearly always preserved in liquid, and often rubber or plastic molds or casts are made of them while they are still in lifelike poses. Insects are generally dried and placed in glassine envelopes or boxes filled with a dry crystalline preservative, such as moth ball crystals.

Broad-margined Grass Yellow Butterfly

Taxidermy, which comes directly from Greek words meaning "arrangement of the skin," generally refers to a "lifelike arrangement." This work has become an advanced art under the hands of certain skilled people. But, in the jungle, only initial or crude taxidermy is used as a means of preservation. Later—even years later—these field-prepared skins can be transformed into a mounted specimen which closely resembles the live animal.

Clytus:
Long-horned
Beetle

The final step in field preparation is to pack securely each "alcoholic," as liquid-preserved specimens are known, in a separate wrapping of cheesecloth. Then all of these wet specimens are placed in a leakproof container for shipment. The dried skins are removed from the drying boards, and each is carefully wrapped in newspaper with moth crystals. The wrapped specimens are then padded and packed in a waterproof box.

Buprestis:
Beetle

The finished specimens and dried skins are a pitiful display compared to the living animal. But each animal collected by an expedition has a use. Without that use, there can be only meaningless waste and purposeless destruction.

Atlas Moth

Buprestis: Beetle

Lucanus: **Beetle**

Helenita
Blue Butterfly

Purple-spotted Swallowtail Butterfly

White Swallowtail Butterfly

c

Long-ho'

New Guinea Birdwing Butterfly

The Eye of Science

To make a complete study of any region would take r
large numbers of trained men. Each specialist on a smal'
be almost a Jack-of-all-trades. Even though native cc
they are often poor cooks and must be shown hc
properly. And if anyone is injured, the scientist r
act as a doctor. Sometimes first-aid treatment is
tion men must operate and perform actual
necessary that each man can collect specime
ments of science. The eye of science is ever
history, and many new things are disc
specialists but who do take the trouble

Our expedition does not have
Nor do we have a trained botanist
these things at any odd moment
special native boys are employ
interests.

Ever since we first ent
of brightly colored butte
notice the butterflies fi
and because their co'
is one of the world'ş
things which also

Beetles are very colorful, and some grow to gigantic size in the tropics. Spiders are plentiful, and also grow to be quite large. Among the most interesting of spiders is the "bird spider," which builds webs so strong that small birds are snared in them. The "funnel web" spider builds a funnel-shaped web leading down to his nest. He is very poisonous and must be carefully watched when he is collected.

Spiders' eyes sparkle brighter than the most brilliant gems when seen at night under the torchlight. Their eyes are either white or green, while moths' eyes are always red and glow like rubies. Moths, also, are abundant, and the world's largest moth, the Atlas, lives in these New Guinea forests. This giant moth has over an eleven-inch wing span and is beautifully colored in shades of soft brown.

Insects are collected in many ways. Nets of various sorts are used, and at night a funnel of cloth with an open bottle at the bottom is set up under the pressure lamp to collect insects, which are attracted by the light. Placing a white sheet under bushes and then beating the bushes with a stick is another very useful collecting method. And, of course, lifting stones and pulling apart rotten stumps and logs are very necessary tasks.

Insects are usually killed by putting them into a jar containing cyanide crystals, which form a powerful and deadly gas. These jars are always handled very carefully, for this gas is as dangerous to man as it is to insects. After the insects are killed, they are labeled and placed in boxes between layers of cotton. Moth crystals are placed in the boxes to keep live insects from eating the specimens. Spiders are placed in jars containing formaldehyde, for they do not dry satisfactorily. And moths and butterflies are each placed in separate envelopes with their delicate wings folded back.

MOUNTING A BUTTERFLY

The specimen is folded and packed in the field (left), then it is spread, dried, and pinned and labeled for study at the museum.

It is important for animal collectors to also collect plants so that botanists can tell them more about *ecology,* or the study of the surroundings which affect animal life. But plants are difficult to collect, for there are thousands of kinds, and anyone not trained as a botanist does not know what to collect. Because of this, the laboratory botanist trains the collector in botanical techniques before the expedition leaves the museum. The field scientist studies similar specimens and carries sketches and photographs to help him properly gather ecological material.

Botanical specimens are sometimes put into formaldehyde and preserved as animals are. But usually they are pressed and dried and taken to the museum flattened between large sheets of absorbent paper. Photographs and artist's sketches are also very important, because pressed flowers and leaves always fade and lose their shape.

The jungle is filled with flowers. Orchids festoon the mossy branches of the trees and hang in lovely clusters from the treetops. Bright colors and sweet scents are a part of the jungle landscape. Strangler vines creep up the trees and hang like a ship's rigging wherever you walk. Leaves of every size and description nod and sway back and forth as shining drops of water strike them and run off. Nearly all jungle plants and flowers are strange to us. Many are beautiful, but some are filled with thorns.

There is one tree the natives all carefully avoid. That is the "stinging tree." This tree has heart-shaped leaves with a fuzzy coating that hides thousands of poisonous barbs covering the surface. If anyone touches or brushes his arm against these leaves he is painfully poisoned, and the poisoning has been known to cause death.

The field collector can never be blinded by his personal enthusiasms. He must apply himself with an equal vigor to the collection of anything which might in any way help his fellow workers or his fellow man.

A Vanishing Life

Natives in faraway tropical countries are often thought of as strange, dark-skinned people who wear few clothes and are always savage. Nothing could be less true. They are not educated, but they are certainly not "inferior." They have mothers and fathers whom they love and respect, family traditions, and very strict laws. They own property and work for their living. Actually, their ways and traditions are far older than ours. For their traditions are elemental—springing from the first and most simple ways of doing things. It is we who have changed, not they. Our way is the new way, and is changing every day. Their way has not changed in thousands of years.

The thing which interests us is that these opposite ways of living exist side by side today; but very soon this will not be so. The simple way of life is fast disappearing. Our ways are enveloping the native ways, and soon there will be little to tell us apart. The native's rituals, his songs and traditions, his art and handiwork, and even his tools and methods of using them will soon be gone. One of the prime purposes of an expedition penetrating into the last strongholds of native ways and culture is not to bring back "curiosities" or to collect unusual things which are different from our own; rather, it is to preserve for future generations these remnants of native life which will soon disappear forever.

We leave our camp on a bright morning and walk northward up the valley. There are no villages near our camp because the land is not as good for native crops as the more fertile valley. Our path runs along the edge of the Rain Forest, overlooking the grassy valley floor. Soon we come upon signs of ownership; certain fruit trees and palms are marked with notches or woven strips of grass. All native people honor these signs, and there is little stealing from, or harm done to, another's property.

After many hours of walking, we come upon the first village. Children and dogs are always first to know of our coming, and there is a wild clamor of loud cries and frenzied barking to welcome us. In some parts of New Guinea natives are still hostile to any stranger, but in most places the people act in the same manner we would if strange-looking people came to our town. We would first be curious and then, if the strangers were friendly, everyone would start asking questions. That is just what usually happens in native villages: fierce-looking warriors in paint and feathers, carrying deadly weapons, are curious, but at first distant. If we show ourselves to be friendly, there are many smiles and everyone starts asking questions in his own tongue. If we should appear hostile, there is always the possibility that we might be in danger. There are still tribal wars where spears and arrows are used to deadly advantage, and there are still white settlers with old arrow wounds.

The villagers are often shy about cameras. They think that a box with an eye in it is "puri-puri," or magic, and will cast a spell on them. But once they see the picture of their own faces on paper, they think that it is a good magic and want to be in every picture you try to take. They all rush in front of your camera and stand stiffly at attention, scowl, and look "manly" until they hear the magic click which they know to mean it's all over; they then all begin to giggle and jabber, each telling the other how much better *he* looked. A favorite trick in studying these people is to have someone pretend to take a picture, making a great show of aiming and snapping. Then, when the show is over and everyone relaxes, the real pictures are taken by someone else standing on the edge of it all.

Kinds of New Guinea Money

Small Shell

Stone Ax

Arm Shell

Bird of Paradise Plumes

Money Cowrie

Shell Necklace

Besides photographs, many diagrams, sketches, and notes are made of village life. One sees many small activities, such as little boys catching butterflies with ingenious nets made of a forked stick which has been passed through many webs of the large bird spider. Once caught, the large butterflies are often secured by a long strand of fine grass or web to fly along with the child, much as a dog is kept on a leash. The children make fine pinwheels of palm leaves, and throwing two-foot-long grass stalks at a target is a favorite game. They become very accurate with these darts and play happily for hours in the warm sun.

The women of the village do most of the gardening and most of the work. They pound taro root, dig sweet potatoes, and collect native fruits. They cook over hot stones, which are heated in a pit hollowed out in the earth. The food is placed on large banana leaves on top of these stones; then everything is heavily covered over with more leaves and grass. The food is cooked by the steam created by the wet leaves placed over the heated stones. When the top leaves are taken off, the food is found to be quite clean and nicely flavored. Meat, however, is cooked in a manner not to our liking. When a possum or other animal is killed, it is simply thrown whole on an open fire—head, tail, and all. The hair burns off, and the rest cooks and splits open. The whole of it—bones and not a few leaves and sticks—is then cut up and mixed with vegetables.

The village men spend much time hunting and gathering together in men's "clubs," where women are not allowed. They do most of the ritual dancing and spend hours preparing themselves with elaborate paint and brilliant feathers for these events. They also make drums and prepare spears and hunting arrows. Many of their axes and cutting tools are still made of stone, and these must be patiently chipped and formed.

Births, deaths, weddings, and many other occasions are made the object of elaborate feasts and traditional rituals. Many days are spent in preparation, and when the Great Day actually arrives, the feast may last for two or three days or even a week. A dancing ground is often kept, where the earth is pounded down so evenly that it resembles shining brown glass. The colorful splendor of these ceremonies is unforgettable. The sound of the drums and the picture of the firelight casting long shadows on the elaborately dressed natives are never to be forgotten. Soon all this will fade away and be replaced by the white man's ways.

As we roam through the village we ask our guide if anyone would like to trade his belongings for things which we have brought with us. He announces our wishes to the people, and soon all manner of things are being brought in for our inspection. We are interested in nearly everything they have, and buy examples of many. There are stone axheads, combs, spears, arrows, dishes of wood, necklaces, drums, flutes, ornaments, and ebony statues of their gods. Here in this secluded valley we pay for these items with colored beads, soap, wire, nails, medicines, and trade tobacco, which is smoked in long cigarettes made of rolled newspaper. The newspaper itself is very valuable and is used as an important item of trade. But in preserving the things of this simple life we are at the same time hastening its destruction. As the natives acquire more and more of the white man's ways, they are quick to forget their own.

Natives are not necessarily backward people; they have simply not developed beyond many of the simple instincts. In a few short months a native who has lived all his life by bows and arrows and stone axes can be taught to drive a tractor or to use a typewriter. These people, some of whose fathers were cannibals and ate "long pig," as human flesh was called, are being taught new things by a government which cares about their future. Before many years, these people will rule their own country and become a part of the world community. This land was made a natural paradise of warm rich earth and many resources, but now it is an awakening paradise. The old ways are still alive today, but children of the future will know about them only from books and museums.

Bat Caves and Orchids

Back at our base camp we continue with the daily routine of study and collecting. After a month of hard work in our first area, we send for native carriers and transport all the equipment to a new camp, three thousand feet higher up the valley wall. The same collecting methods at this higher location secure many new and different specimens which are not to be found near the valley floor. And after another month, we again move camp, this time to a point far up the valley at a still higher elevation. Other camps are made for shorter periods in different kinds of forests.

At one of our last camps, on the spur of a mountain range far distant from our first base camp, we learn from passing natives that there are many limestone caves in the area. Such caves are of much interest, for they are often the home of rare bats and frequently contain strange forms of subterranean life.

The caves are located at the source of a large stream which tumbles down from the high ledges beyond our new camp. It is a long and tiring walk, for the jungle is so thick on either side of the stream that we must walk in the water and scramble over the wet rocks.

During our walk we come upon what seems a forest of orchids. These lovely plants are of a type which grows as an "air plant," taking its strength to live and grow from the air around it. The roots of the plant grow where the tiny seeds fall on branches of trees. They are delicate and beautiful flowers, and thousands of sprays of them hang in cascades as we move upstream.

Finally we reach the cave. The entrance is a few hundred feet above the stream, and we must climb nearly straight up to reach it. The climb has made us very warm, and the drafts of air which come from the black depths of the cave are cool and refreshing. Our own native boys make torches of grass and sticks and prepare to start down with us. But the natives who live nearby refuse to go inside, saying that it is "tambu" and that "puri-puri," or black magic, is in the cave. Being now used to native superstitions, we do not press them. We adjust our headlights and start to descend the steep slope which leads downward.

As we leave the daylight and enter this world of darkness, all sound ceases. We stop for breath and can hear only our breathing and our heartbeats. We walk carefully between deep, green pools of water and our

Dobsonia: Bare-backed Fruit Bat

headlights pick out the rose-colored stalactites that hang from the high ceiling and are reflected in the pools. There are narrow passageways leading into great cavernous rooms, and different strata and colors of the stone show how the water has carved the limestone.

Suddenly we notice a movement of the air and hear a faint roaring sound. As our lights cut through the blackness, we see hundreds of eyes which glow like coals against the almost invisible ceiling. It is very eerie knowing we are deep in the earth under millions of tons of stone. The blackness seems more black, and an icy chill runs up our backs. The natives become frightened and want to go back. But we explain that the burning red eyes are only the eyes of hundreds of bats, hanging upside down from the high, vaulted roof. As we approach, they are frightened by the lights and begin to fly. There are so many that soon the air is a whirl of hurtling bodies and the beat of their wings becomes a confusing din as loud as thunder. The bats are all around us in great waves, but not one ever touches us. Their sensitive hearing organs turn them just inches away from our heads.

The bats are of two kinds. One is a bare-backed bat with a wing-spread of about two feet. His name is *Dobsonia;* he is a fruit-eating bat that lives near the entrances of caves. He is black and has an intelligent face, like that of a terrier. The other is a smaller, insect-eating bat named *Miniopterus,* or the "bent-winged" bat. This bat is brown and has wings that are peculiar, in that they bend forward when he is at rest. There are many thousands of the smaller kind, and we sink nearly to our knees in the accumulated guano of many years.

We collect enough specimens to make an adequate scientific series and go on to explore the cave. Although we search thoroughly, we find no "puri-puri."

Miniopterus: Bent-winged Bat

***Pteropus:* Spectacled Flying Fox**

As we climb out of the cool cave, the hot, sweet breath of the jungle seems overpowering. We wish we could wait until just before dark, for then we could see a great, roaring cloud of bats emerge from the cave entrance and fan out over the thick jungle in search of food. But we must hurry back because we want to see the "flying fox" camps.

Flying foxes are not foxes at all, but giant fruit bats. They are the largest bats in the world. Their wingspread can reach nearly six feet. They are one of the truly remarkable sights of the jungle night, for they fly slowly and silently with only an occasional flapping sound. Their voices, however, are raucous, and they scream sharply at one another in the swaying treetops. For a bat, they are prettily colored—soft brown and gold. Their large eyes and intelligent faces make them appear friendly, but you must keep well away from their sharp teeth. These giant flying foxes live in the tops of tall trees (unlike their cave-dwelling cousins) in what are called "camps." Their noisy clamor can be heard over a mile away.

Although we are now heavily laden with specimens, we come upon yet another creature before we reach our camp. Over the path leading from the stream we hear a sharp, sweet whistle. The whistler proves to be another bat, and he appears to be the strangest of them all. He is the tube-nosed bat, named *Nyctimene,* after the Greek goddess of night. He is light tan in color, with yellow spots on his wings and a dark stripe on his back. But the strangest thing about him is that his yellow nose ends in two "tubes." This highly specialized animal is thought to have gained such a nose from his habit of eating soft fruit. Nature apparently evolved this system to prevent his getting food caught in his breathing system.

One of the boys has carried back some of the lovely orchids from the orchid forest. In the light of the pressure lamp he places them beside this grotesque new bat. The contrast is not so strange as we would have thought, for we see that the bat has a peculiar beauty of its own, and in the warm depths of this dark forest he is at home, while we are the strangers.

Nyctimene: Tube-nosed Bat

51

Kione, Taubada!

Among the many things that must be done by a field scientist, the making of exact notes about the many things he collects is most important. And if he can make sketches and drawings in the field, it is much to his advantage. Photographs are very valuable, but taking fine photographs is time-consuming, and proper lighting and backgrounds have to be considered. Color sketches can be made hurriedly and often can be developed into finished drawings or paintings later on.

Sketching is a gentle enough pastime. That is, it is, ordinarily. But even the most harmless of jobs can be dangerous in the jungle. Our ornithologist, his arm resting on a stone as he sketches the nest of a bowerbird, is bitten by a scorpion. He is soon unconscious and his native assistant runs into camp, loudly crying for help. We race back over the forest track and apply the same treatment as for snakebite. The victim is kept warm and soon recovers, but for a while he is very sick.

Accidents of a more serious nature are rare, for great care is taken to avoid them. But they do happen. One of the native boys, using an ax, accidentally slashes his leg. He is bleeding in bright spurts, so we know he has severed an artery. Soon he is in shock and falls unconscious. Something must be done immediately. We quickly tie the artery and then suture it with a surgical needle. It is an emergency and we must use our scientific forceps. We boil them and then sew up the outside skin. We are poor surgeons, but the boy's life is saved. Soon he is well enough to be carried out to a doctor.

The daily routine of collecting usually continues until just before the expedition is to end. We have been in contact with our agents at Port Moresby and with the company whose plane flew us into the mountains. Now we must make arrangements to leave. Instead of returning to the airstrip where we arrived, which is now nearly a hundred miles away, we arrange to have the plane land on a grassy spot near our final camp.

The last day of the expedition arrives. The last specimen is numbered and packed. The camp is taken down and once again packed, but this time for air travel; vats of preservative are double-checked to be certain no moisture can penetrate them. On occasion the entire work of an expedition has been lost because of careless handling. We check, and then, over and over, we check again.

We watch anxiously as the plane bounces over our homemade airstrip and comes, finally, to a stop. Our equipment is packed aboard the plane, care being taken to lash it down thoroughly with ropes. We say our good-bys to our many good native friends and then quickly rise up into the clouds and are gone. Leave-taking is always hurried—for at any moment the clouds may settle and the pilot may be unable to see the dangerous peaks.

Once back at Port Moresby, there are the same formalities of government to attend to as when we arrived. We say farewell to our loyal native staff, which served us so faithfully and well, and the simple words of good-by—"kione, Taubada!"—are the last words of Motu that we will hear for a long time. Soon we are again aboard the ship and preparing for the long trip home.

Background to an Expedition

Expeditions have been going afield since history began. The Phoenicians, Egyptians, Greeks, and Romans in ancient times not only waged war and commerce but also sent out exploratory expeditions. Later the Spanish, French, and English organized expeditions to the furthermost places of the earth. Spain laid claim to America, and a Dutchman named Abel Tasman discovered Australia. France's famous Admiral Jean François de Lapérouse explored much of the South Seas, and England's Captain Cook sailed round the world on many voyages of discovery.

As America grew from the small holdings on the east coast, expeditions were sent into the wild interior. Cartier and Father Marquette and Lewis and Clark all made valuable discoveries.

Among the most famous of natural history expeditions was Charles Darwin's journey aboard the *Beagle* in 1831. Darwin surveyed the South American coasts, the Galapagos Islands, Tahiti, New Zealand, Australia, and many small islands and coastlines on this long voyage of exploration and study. The expedition took five full years, and Darwin's discoveries and observations on this voyage were later to become world famous in his theories on natural selection and man's origins. Since then, there have been many expeditions, large and small, to all corners of the world. Dr. Roy Chapman Andrews discovered dinosaur eggs in the Gobi Desert and Dr. James Chapin penetrated into the heart of the African Congo.

But no matter how large or how small an expedition, once home again, the collecting phase is over. However, the final results of the expedition may not be brought to a conclusion for many months or years. The specimens are all neatly stored in airtight and insectproof cases in the different departments to which they belong. They are permanently catalogued and separated in preparation for research.

The specimens are no longer a "collection," but are in different parts of the museum—and are even sent to other museums, both in America and in Europe. The research is now not restricted by the quickened pace of field activity. There is much time, and time is used lavishly at this stage, for hasty conclusions are seldom worth while. The same painstaking checking and rechecking goes on and on. Parasitologists carefully study the "ectoparasites," or external parasites, such as mites, ticks, and fleas, as well as the internal parasites which have been preserved with the whole specimens. Taxonomists, or specialists interested in the correct classification of things according to their natural relationship, study the skulls and other hard parts. There can be a hundred or more separate studies undertaken simultaneously on a mere handful of small specimens. Hospitals, universities, departments of agriculture, libraries, and many other vital institutions are among those which will study and benefit from our expedition. And, in addition, certain specimens may be "mounted" through the art of taxidermy and placed in educational exhibits in museums.

. . . .

An expedition does not begin as an idea in someone's mind, as would a "safari," or hunting trip. Rather than a beginning, an expedition is usually the *end* of many months or perhaps years of study on a subject. When all available research material on a subject is exhausted, new material must be gathered.

Months of careful planning are essential. If the area chosen is in a foreign country, permits must be obtained. All passports and customs

55

declarations must be in order. Transportation, whether by air, land, or sea, must be arranged many months in advance. Long lists of equipment must be purchased and organized down to the last detail.

Packing is an art, and expert packing is learned only through experience. Every box is numbered, every item is labeled and listed in duplicate, and each is carefully packed away. Tents, cooking utensils, axheads —everything down to the smallest screw and hypodermic needle is listed and packed where it can be opened and used at a moment's notice. Guns must be greased and taken apart. Ammunition must be counted and careful estimates made as to how much will be used.

Medical supplies, drugs, scissors, scalpels, thread, insecticide, wax, shoe laces, and a hundred small and obscure items must all be estimated, counted, separated, and finally packed.

As the date for sailing approaches, much still remains to be done. There are cargo manifests, customs permits, shipments by truck to the pier, insurance, and numerous other details. There are endless hypodermic "shots" for tetanus, yellow fever, cholera, and smallpox. And there are medical checkups, dentist appointments, and legal papers to arrange.

This is the story of but one kind of an expedition. Some expeditions may soon be going far out of sight beyond the stars . . . and others, still valid "expeditions," may go only as far as the corner field to watch the habits of meadow mice. An expedition is a "freeing of the mind" as well as a freeing of the foot. Superstitions, whether in the mind of a native or in our own minds, are a waste of time. Bats are not "blind," owls are not "wise," and black cats are not "bad luck." There are quite enough genuine difficulties and problems facing this new world of science without adding superstitions. We must keep a clear eye and an inquiring mind if we wish to join the ranks of those who go far afield and *do* things. Or else we must remain at home and drag our traps.